This Book Belongs To:

_____

Library of Congress Cataloging-in-Publication Data available.

Printed in China

ISBN: 978-0-578-79324-5

Book design and illustrations by Christine Diaz

JKL Teahouse LLC
www.jklteahouse.com

R is for Rice

By Susan Hsia Lew, Joanna Kong, & Nithin Jilla
Written by Susan Hsia Lew
Illustrated by Christine Diaz

For Henry and Jesse

- Susan Hsia Lew

To my mom and dad

- Joanna Kong

To my parents, the future generations, and all those
who inspired me to adventure toward my dreams

- Nithin Jilla

Are you ready, are you set,
to read a delicious alphabet?

A

is for Asia and America alike, and the Asian flavors in American life.

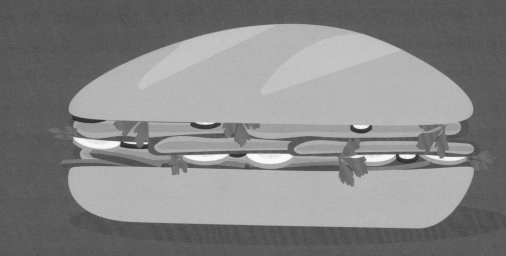

B

is for Bibimbap, Bento, Bánh Mì,

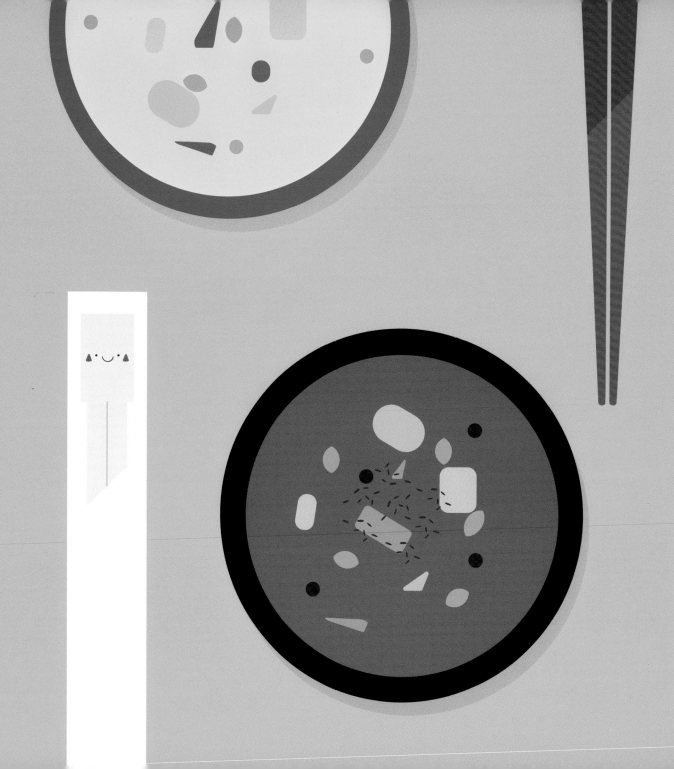

is for Chopsticks
and steamy Curry!

is for Dumplings served
so many ways,

is for Egg Rolls
and steamed Edamame!

F

You are worth a fortune to me!

8 8 8 8 8

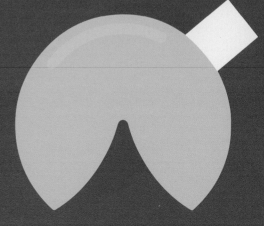

You are one smart cookie!

is for Fortune Cookies for me,

is for Green Tea
and grilled Galbi.

is for Hot, Hot, Hot Sauces and spices,

is for Idli in all different sizes!

is for Jasmine, which
makes a great tea,

K

is for Kung Pao Chicken and Kimchi!

L

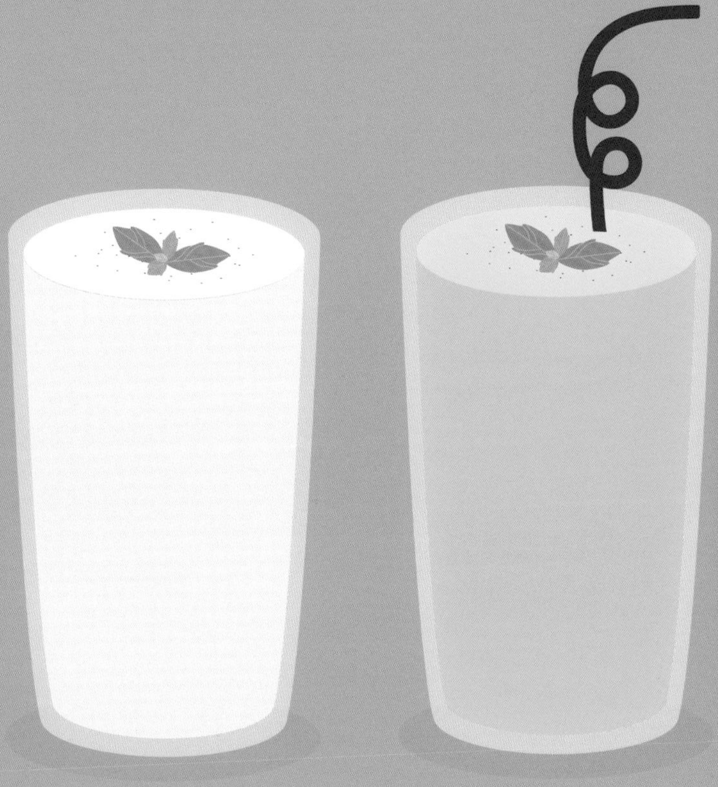

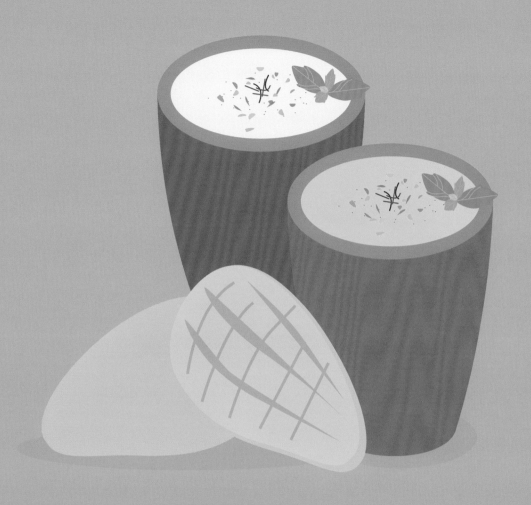

is for Lassi, my favorite treat,

is for Matcha and the
Mochi I eat!

is for Nori and freshly
baked Naan,

is for Orange Chicken,
that's nearly all gone!

is for Poke, Pad Thai, and Pho,

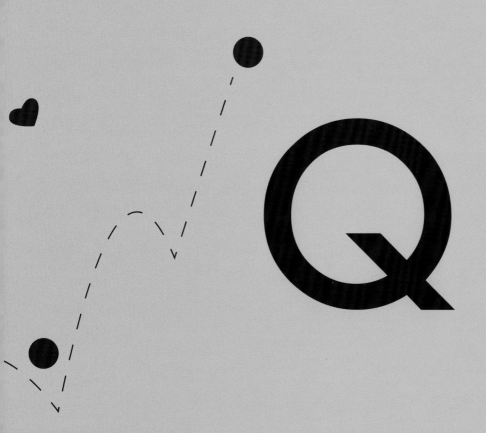

is for QQ, the "bite" of boba!

R

is for Rice — Basmati and Sticky,

S

is for Samosa,
Soy Sauce, and Sushi!

is for Tandoori Chicken
so yummy,

U

is for Udon noodles
in my tummy!

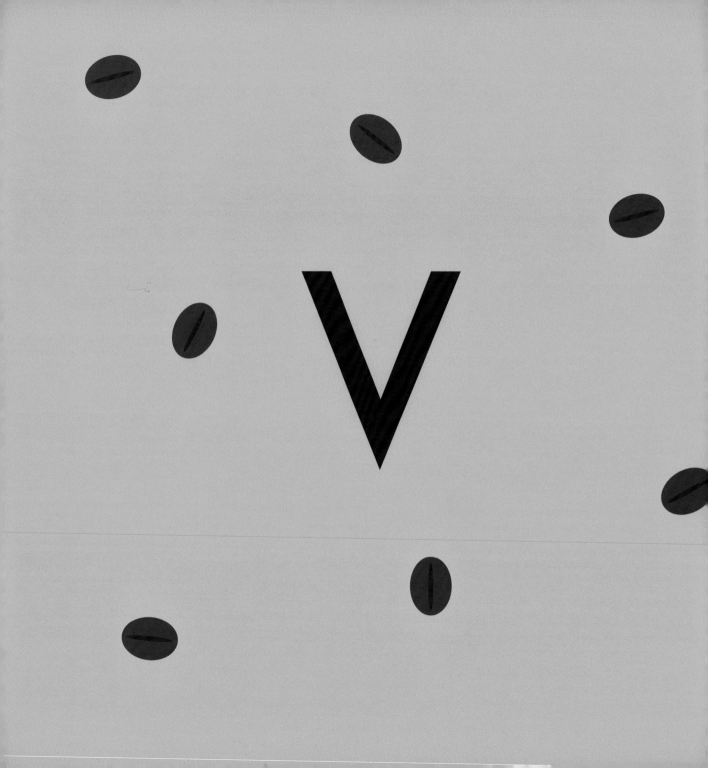

is for Vietnamese Coffee with ice,

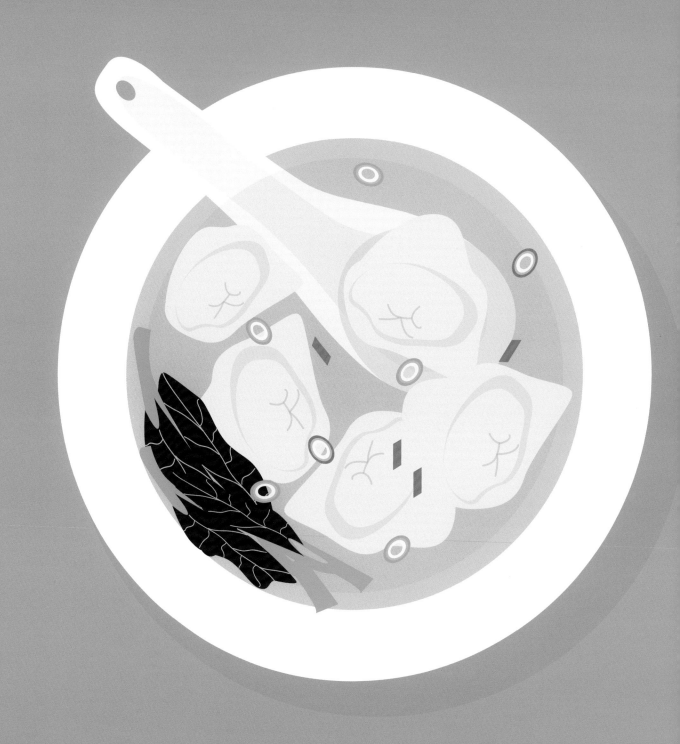

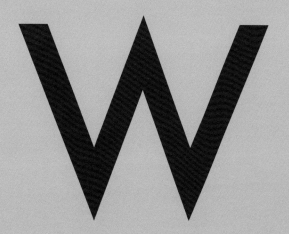

is for Wontons I eat
in one bite!

is for Xiao Long Bao,
soupy delights,

is for Yakisoba, noodles
stir fried!

Z

is for Zen, the feeling of peace, knowing Asian Americans gave us such good things to eat!

The End

Turn the page for a pronunciation guide!

Pronunciation Guide

Letter	Name	Pronunciation
B	Bibimbap	bee-beem-BAHP
	Bento	BEN-toh
	Bánh Mì	buhn-MEE
C	Chopsticks	CHAHP-stiks
	Curry	KUH-ree
D	Dumpling	DUHM-pling
E	Edamame	eh-duh-MAH-may
	Eggroll	EGH-rohl
F	Fortune Cookie	FAWR-chuhn KOO-kee
G	Green Tea	green tee
	Galbi	GAHL-bee
H	Hot Sauce	HAHT sahss
I	Idli	ID-lee
J	Jasmine	JAZ-muhn
K	Kung Pao Chicken	kuhng pao CHIK-uhn
	Kimchi	KIM-chee
L	Lassi	LAH-see
M	Matcha	MAH-chuh
	Mochi	MOH-chee

Pronunciation Guide

Letter	Name	Pronunciation
N	Nori	NOHR-ee
	Naan	nahn
O	Orange Chicken	AWR-inj-CHIK-uhn
	Poke	POH-kay
P	Pad Thai	pad-TIE
	Pho	fuh
Q	QQ	KEW-kew
	Rice	rhyss
R	Basmati Rice	bahs-MAH-tee
	Sticky Rice	STIH-kee rhyss
	Samosa	sa-MO-sa
S	Soy Sauce	SOI-saws
	Sushi	SOO-shee
T	Tandoori Chicken	tahn-DUR-ee CHIK-uhn
U	Udon Noodles	OO-don
V	Vietnamese Coffee	vee-yet-nah-MEEZ KAW-fee
W	Wonton	WON-ton
X	Xiao Long Bao	shao-lohng-BAO
Y	Yakisoba	yah-kee-SOH-bah